A MESSAGE TO PARENTS

It is of vital importance for adults to read good books to young children in order to aid their psychological and intellectual development. As well as stimulating the child's imagination, it creates a positive relationship between adult and child. Reading aloud will also help children to increase their basic vocabulary and encourage them to begin reading alone. Brown.Watson has published this series of books with these aims in mind. By collecting this inexpensive library, adults and children can share hours of pleasurable reading.

Printed in the E.C.

Christmas Carols, Songs and Verses

Illustrated by Stephen Holmes

ENGLAND

WE THREE KINGS OF ORIENT ARE

We three kings of Orient are.
Bearing gifts, we traverse afar-
Field and fountain,
Moor and mountain-
Following yonder star.

CHORUS:

Oh, star of wonder, star of night,
Star of royal beauty bright,
Westward leading, still proceeding,
Guide us to thy perfect light.

THE TWELVE DAYS OF CHRISTMAS

On the first day of Christmas
My true love sent to me
A partridge in a pear tree.

On the second day of Christmas
My true love sent to me
Two turtle doves.

On the third day of Christmas
My true love sent to me
Three French hens.

On the fourth day of Christmas
My true love sent to me
Four calling birds.

On the fifth day of Christmas
My true love sent to me
Five gold rings.

On the sixth day of Christmas
My true love sent to me
Six geese a-laying.

On the seventh day of Christmas
My true love sent to me
Seven swans a-swimming.

On the eighth day of Christmas
My true love sent to me
Eight maids a-milking.

On the ninth day of Christmas
My true love sent to me
Nine drummers drumming.

On the tenth day of Christmas
My true love sent to me
Ten pipers piping.

On the eleventh day of Christmas
My true love sent to me
Eleven ladies dancing.

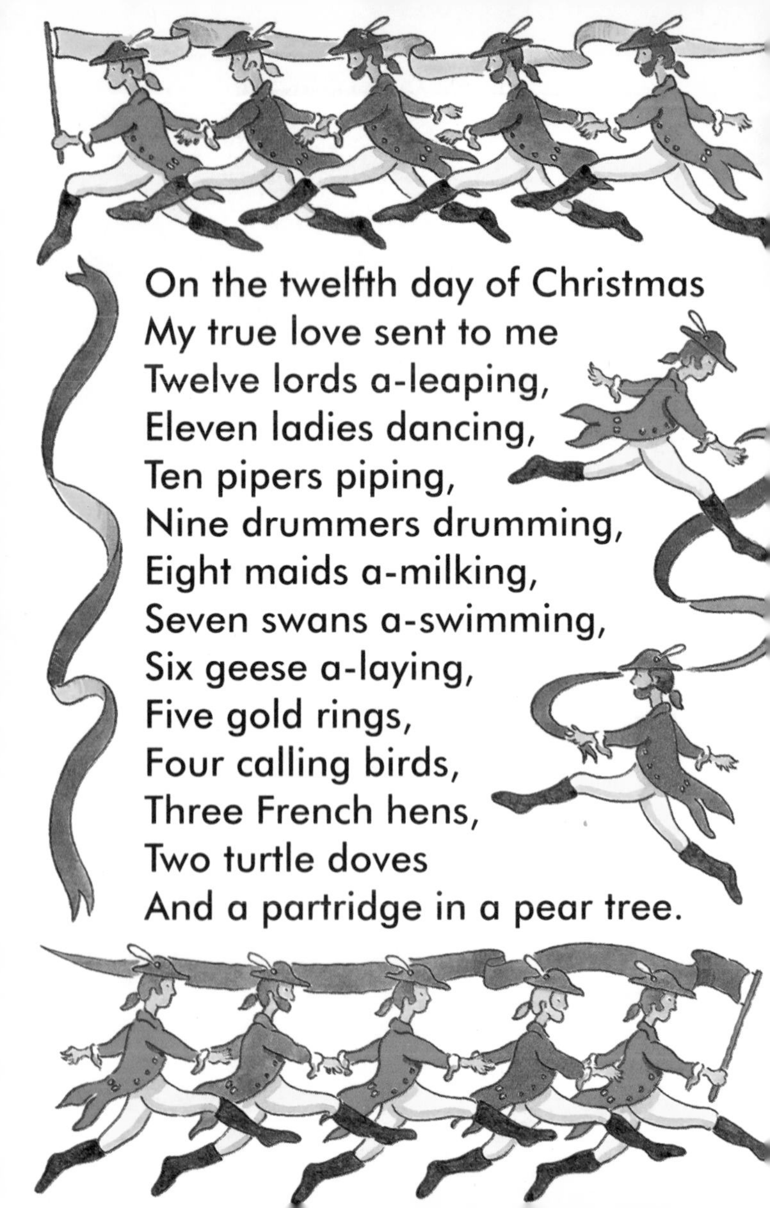

On the twelfth day of Christmas
My true love sent to me
Twelve lords a-leaping,
Eleven ladies dancing,
Ten pipers piping,
Nine drummers drumming,
Eight maids a-milking,
Seven swans a-swimming,
Six geese a-laying,
Five gold rings,
Four calling birds,
Three French hens,
Two turtle doves
And a partridge in a pear tree.

ONCE IN ROYAL DAVID'S CITY

Once in Royal David's City
Stood a lowly cattle shed,
Where a mother laid her baby
In a manger for His bed;
Mary was that mother mild,
Jesus Christ her little child.

ALL YEAR ROUND

When Spring-time comes,
There's lots to do -
Watching birds and squirrels, too.
Flying kites and pressing flowers,
Now there are more daylight hours.

Summer-time! And, to keep cool,
We play in my big paddling pool!
Picnic lunches, games outside -
Scooters, tricycles to ride.

Autumn now, and all around,
Leaves come fluttering to the ground.
Bonfires, conkers to collect,
And the wild birds to protect.

Winter comes with frost and snow,
We think of someone we all know
Coming down a chimney stack ...
Can you guess what's in his sack?

JINGLE BELLS

Dashing through the snow
In a one horse open sleigh,
O'er the fields we go,
Laughing all the way;
Bells on bob-tail ring,
Making spirits bright,

What fun it is to ride and sing
A sleighing song tonight!
Jingle bells! Jingle balls!
Jingle all the way!
Oh, what fun it is to ride
In a one horse open sleigh!

AWAY IN A MANGER

Away in a manger,
No crib for a bed,
The little Lord Jesus
Laid down His sweet head;

The stars in the bright sky
Look down where He lay,
The little Lord Jesus
Asleep on the hay.

TEDDY'S FAVOURITES

What does a Teddy Bear like best?
Perhaps you'd like to know!
Well...swings and whirly roundabouts
And a bouncy ball to throw...

Currant buns and chocolate,
Honey spread on bread,
And listening to a story,
When I'm tucked up in bed.

Sandcastles! Iced lollipops!
A friendly dog or cat!
Listening to the rain outside
As it goes pitter-pat...

Fireside chats when winter comes...
A gift from Santa Claus...
I think that's all my favourite things.
Can you tell me some of yours?

THE HOLLY AND THE IVY

The holly and the ivy,
When they are both full grown,
Of all the trees that are in the wood,
The holly bears the crown.

CHORUS:
The rising of the sun
And the running of the deer,
The playing of the merry organ,
Sweet singing in the choir.

The holly bears a berry,
As red as any blood,
And Mary bore sweet Jesus Christ
To do poor sinners good.

The holly bears a prickle,
As sharp as any thorn,
And Mary bore sweet Jesus Christ
On Christmas Day in the morn.

The holly bears a bark,
As bitter as any gall,
And Mary bore sweet Jesus Christ
For to redeem us all.

I SAW THREE SHIPS

I saw three ships come sailing in,
On Christmas Day, on Christmas Day,
I saw three ships come sailing in,
On Christmas Day in the morning.

And what was in those ships all three?
On Christmas Day, on Christmas Day,
And what was in those ships all three?
On Christmas Day in the morning.

Our Lord Jesus Christ and his lady,
On Christmas Day, on Christmas Day,
Our Lord Jesus Christ and his lady,
On Christmas Day in the morning.

GOD REST YE MERRY GENTLEMEN

God rest ye merry gentlemen:
Let nothing you dismay.
Remember, Christ our Saviour
Was born on Christmas Day,
To save us all from Satan's power
When we were gone astray.

CHORUS:
Oh, tidings of comfort and joy,
Comfort and joy,
Oh, tidings of comfort and joy!

OH COME, ALL YE FAITHFUL

Oh come, all ye faithful,
Joyful and triumphant,
Oh come ye,
Oh come ye to Bethlehem.
Come and behold Him,
Born the King of Angels

CHORUS:

Oh come, let us adore Him,
Oh come, let us adore Him,
Oh come, let us adore Him,
Christ the Lord!